GRADE

C000129453

£8.95

The 2005–2007 Syllabus
requirements, especially
sight-reading. Attention
Notices on the inside fro_
any changes.

The syllabus is obtainable from music retailers or from
the Services Department, The Associated Board of the Royal
Schools of Music, 24 Portland Place, London W1B 1LU,
United Kingdom (please send a stamped addressed C5
(162mm × 229mm) envelope).

In exam centres outside the UK, information and syllabuses
may be obtained from the Local Representative.

CONTENTS

page

LIST A

1   **Girolamo Alessandro Frescobaldi** (1583–1643) Canzona seconda   2

2   **Simon Leduc** (1742–77) Grazioso: Sonata in A, Op. 4 No. 5, second movement   4

3   **Antonio Vivaldi** (1678–1741) Allegro: Sonata in G minor, RV 28, second movement   6

LIST B

1   **Carl Bohm** (1844–1920) Bolero, No. 9 from *Albumblätter*   8

2   **Antonín Dvořák** (1841–1904) Larghetto: Sonatina in G, Op. 100, second movement   10

3   **Zdeněk Fibich** (1850–1900) Allegro moderato: Sonatina in D minor, Op. 27,   12
    first movement

LIST C

1   **Manuel de Falla** (1876–1946) El paño moruno, No. 1 from *Siete canciones populares*   14
    españolas

2   **Lee Burswold** Blues #1, from *Two Blues*   16

3   **William Walton** (1902–83) Canzonetta, No. 1 from *Two Pieces for Violin and Piano*   18

Where appropriate, pieces in this volume have been checked with original source material and
edited as necessary for instructional purposes. Any editorial additions to the texts are given in
small print, within square brackets, or – in the case of slurs and ties – in the form ⌒. Fingering,
phrasing, bowing, metronome marks and the editorial realization of ornaments (where given)
are for guidance only; they are not comprehensive or obligatory.

DO NOT
PHOTOCOPY
© MUSIC

Alternative pieces for this grade

LIST A

4   **attrib. Handel** Adagio and Allegro: Sonata in E, Op. 1 No. 15, HWV 373, 1st and 2nd movts. Handel, *Complete Works for Violin and
    Basso Continuo* (Bärenreiter)

5   **Mozart** Andante (without cadenza; violin tacet in tuttis): Concerto No. 2 in D, K. 211, 2nd movt (Henle or Henle–Schott/MDS or
    Bärenreiter)

6   **Tessarini** Allegro: Concerto in G, Op. 1 No. 3, 1st movt (Boosey & Hawkes)

LIST B

4   **Dancla** Mazurka, No. 20 from *Petite école de la mélodie*, Op. 123, Vol. 3 (Schott/MDS)

5   **Grieg** Wiegenlied (Berceuse, Op. 38 No. 1). *Singende Geige (Singing Violin)*, Book 3, arr. Doleżal (PWM/MDS)

6   **Simonetti** Madrigale (Ricordi/UMP)

LIST C

4   **Lennox Berkeley** Elegy for violin and piano, Op. 33 No. 2. Berkeley, *Elegy and Toccata* (Chester/Music Sales)

5   **Peter Maxwell Davies** Mrs Linklater's Tune for Solo Violin (Chester/Music Sales)

6   **Martinů** Rhythmical Studies, No. 2 in 5/8 (*with piano accompaniment*) (Schott/MDS)

© 2004 by The Associated Board of the Royal Schools of Music

No part of this publication may be copied or reproduced in
any form or by any means without the prior permission of
the publisher.

Music origination by Andrew Jones.
Cover by Økvik Design.
Printed in England by Caligraving Ltd,
Thetford, Norfolk.

A:1

Canzona seconda

Edited by
Richard Jones

FRESCOBALDI

Girolamo Alessandro Frescobaldi (1583–1643) was the greatest organist of his day and the most influential Italian keyboard composer of the 17th century. The *Canzoni* of 1628, dedicated to the Grand Duke of Tuscany, were his only published collection of instrumental ensemble music. In this second canzona, the sharp contrasts between sections need to be brought out by the player, with the fast and lively Allegro sections crisply articulated, and the gentler, more yielding Adagio passages much more smoothly bowed. The lightest touch should be reserved for the triple-time passages. The dynamics of the last 12 bars are authentic, but all other dynamics and all slurs and staccato dots are editorial suggestions only.
Sources: *Il primo libro delle Canzoni* (Rome, 1628); *Canzoni da sonare* (Venice, 1634)

A:2

Grazioso

Second movement from Sonata in A, Op. 4 No. 5

Edited by
Richard Jones

LEDUC

Simon Leduc (1742–77) was a Parisian violinist and composer who formed a long and fruitful association with the orchestra of the Concert Spirituel, both as a player and, from 1773, as co-director. *Grazioso* is a minuet in all but name (though in ternary form rather than the more usual binary) and therefore requires a graceful, elegant style of performance, with a certain dance lilt. Given the tempo, the ornaments in b. 38 may be reduced to two notes: upper note–main note (in effect, ignore the *tr* sign).
Source: *Deuxième livre de sonates*, Op. 4 (Paris, 1771)

D.C. al Fine

Allegro

Second movement from Sonata in G minor, RV 28

Edited by
Christian Schneider

VIVALDI

During his lifetime Vivaldi was better known as a violinist than as a composer, although his Italianate style was admired by J. S. Bach, who transcribed several of his concertos. Dynamics are left to the player's discretion. The trills might be played as follows:

b. 13   b. 56

© 1998 by Universal Edition A.G. Wien/UE 17595
Reproduced by permission. All enquiries for this piece apart from the exams should be addressed to Universal Edition (London) Ltd, 48 Great Marlborough Street, London W1F 7BB.

B:1

Bolero

No. 9 from *Albumblätter*

BOHM

The bolero is a Spanish popular dance in triple metre. Its distinctive rhythm is heard here in the right hand of the piano accompaniment.

B:2

Larghetto

Second movement from Sonatina in G, Op. 100

Edited by
Richard Jones

DVOŘÁK

The Sonatina in G, Op. 100, from which this Larghetto is drawn, was written in America in 1893 for the composer's own children to play. The theme of the Larghetto is said to have been inspired by the sight of the beautiful Minnehaha Falls in Minnesota. Certain changes have been made to the bowing for exam purposes. The source has 'meno mosso, tempo primo' at b. 56, but according to the autograph the original tempo and theme return together in b. 72.

Source: *Sonatine für Violine und Pianoforte*, Op. 100 (Berlin: N. Simrock, 1894)

B:3

Allegro moderato

First movement from Sonatina in D minor, Op. 27

Edited by
Richard Jones

FIBICH

Zdeněk Fibich (1850–1900) was, after Smetana and Dvořák, the most prominent Czech composer of the second half of the 19th century. Like most of his chamber music, the Sonatina in D minor, Op. 27, is an early work.
Source: *Sonatina*, Op. 27 (Prague and Leipzig, *c.*1870)

13

El paño moruno

No. 1 from *Siete canciones populares españolas*

Arranged by
Paweł Kochański

FALLA

'El paño moruno' is from a set of seven popular Spanish songs, written for voice and piano by Falla in 1914 and based on Spanish folk material. The title translates as 'The Moorish Cloth'.

All enquiries for this piece apart from the exams should be addressed to G. Ricordi & Co. (London) Ltd, 3rd Floor, Bedford House, 69–79 Fulham High Street, London SW6 3JW.

AB 3006

15

AB 3006

C:2

for Barbara
Blues #1
from *Two Blues*

LEE BURSWOLD

Expressively and tranquilly ♩ = 88

I suggest that Blues #1 be played with quite a bit of freedom against what is generally a recurring, ostinato-like accompaniment. An occasional well-placed portamento could also enhance the 'blues' feel. LB

Lee Burswold (b. 1933) holds a PhD in composition from the Eastman School of Music in Rochester, New York, and is emeritus professor of music at North Park University in Chicago, Illinois. He performs ragtime piano concerts and plays commercial and jazz piano.

to Vivien and Larry

Canzonetta

No. 1 from *Two Pieces for Violin and Piano*

WALTON

C:3

The *Two Pieces for Violin and Piano* date from 1948–50, a period during which Walton concentrated on chamber music and his first opera, *Troilus and Cressida*. The melody that starts at b. 5 is marked in the original edition as being 'based on a troubadour melody', a reference to minstrels of the 11th–13th centuries who flourished in southern France.

© Oxford University Press 1951

Reproduced by permission. All enquiries for this piece apart from the exams should be addressed to Oxford University Press, Great Clarendon Street, Oxford, OX2 6DP.

Checklist of Scales and Arpeggios

Candidates and teachers may find this checklist useful in learning the requirements of the grade. Full details of the forms of the various requirements, including details of rhythms, starting notes and bowing patterns, are given in the syllabus and in the scale books published by the Board.

Grade 6

			separate bows						slurred						
Major Scales									*seven notes to a bow*						
	D♭ Major	2 Octaves													
	F Major	2 Octaves													
	F♯ Major	2 Octaves													
	A Major	3 Octaves													
	B♭ Major	3 Octaves													
Minor Scales (*melodic* and *harmonic*)									*seven notes to a bow*						
	C♯ Minor	2 Octaves													
	F Minor	2 Octaves													
	F♯ Minor	2 Octaves													
	A Minor	3 Octaves													
	B♭ Minor	3 Octaves													
Chromatic Scales									*four* or *six notes to a bow*						
	on A♭	2 Octaves													
	on B	2 Octaves													
	on C	2 Octaves													
Major Arpeggios									*six notes (two-octave arpeggios) and three notes (three-octave arpeggios) to a bow*						
	D♭ Major	2 Octaves													
	F Major	2 Octaves													
	F♯ Major	2 Octaves													
	A Major	3 Octaves													
	B♭ Major	3 Octaves													
Minor Arpeggios									*six notes (two-octave arpeggios) and three notes (three-octave arpeggios) to a bow*						
	C♯ Minor	2 Octaves													
	F Minor	2 Octaves													
	F♯ Minor	2 Octaves													
	A Minor	3 Octaves													
	B♭ Minor	3 Octaves													
Dominant Sevenths									*four notes to a bow*						
	in C	2 Octaves													
	in D	2 Octaves													
	in E♭	2 Octaves													
Diminished Sevenths									*four notes to a bow*						
	on G	2 Octaves													
	on A	2 Octaves													
							refer to syllabus for format								
Double-Stop Scale	in B♭ Major	1 8ve *in sixths*													

11:05